SEEING IS DISBELIEVING

150 ASTOUNDING OPTICAL ILLUSIONS

STERLING INNOVATION

An imprint of Sterling Publishing Co., Inc.

New York / London
www.sterlingpublishing.com

STERLING, the Sterling logo, STERLING INNOVATION, and the Sterling Innovation logo are registered trademarks of Sterling Publishing Co., Inc.

10 9 8 7 6 5 4 3 2 1

Published by Sterling Publishing Co., Inc.
387 Park Avenue South, New York, NY 10016

This book is comprised of materials from the following Sterling Publishing Co., Inc. titles:
Visual Tricks by The Diagram Group © 2001
BrainStrains^{TM} *Great Color Optical Illusions* by Keith Travis © 2002

Distributed in Canada by Sterling Publishing
c/o Canadian Manda Group, 165 Dufferin Street
Toronto, Ontario, Canada M6K 3H6
Distributed in the United Kingdom by GMC Distribution Services
Castle Place, 166 High Street, Lewes, East Sussex, England BN7 1XU
Distributed in Australia by Capricorn Link (Australia) Pty. Ltd.
P.O. Box 704, Windsor, NSW 2756, Australia

Printed in China
All rights reserved

Sterling ISBN 978-1-4027-7581-9

For information about custom editions, special sales, premium and corporate purchases, please contact Sterling Special Sales Department at 800-805-5489 or specialsales@sterlingpublishing.com.

Introduction

Seeing is believing? Not anymore. Open this book at any page and blow your mind! Don't study too many of these brain-bending puzzles at once—it could seriously damage your head. See the impossible; see the incredible; witness the wonderful; seeing is disbelieving! In this book you will find a selection of the world's finest eye-tricking, mind-mangling, brain-bashing puzzles, tricks, and visual oddities. How can a man be happy and sad at the same time? How can a picture make you seasick? When is a straight line bent? Don't know? Look through these pages and watch the paradoxes unfold.

There are hidden objects and lost people to find; mazes to unravel and impossible objects to comprehend. You will have to learn that your eyes are liars if you are going to get through this book without your head melting! Good luck, and remember—when you just can't take any more, all the answers are in the back.

Sherlock Holmes is reading

a headline.

What does it say?

Are you sure?

Is the zebra black with white stripes or
is it white with black stripes?

The name of this old-time print is
"Time Passes." Why do you think it
was given this title?

Can you figure out why this picture is
titled "Before and After Marriage"?

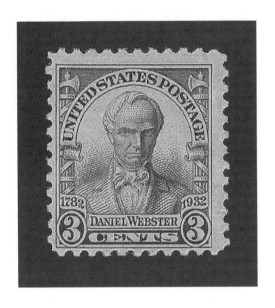

This is a real postage stamp of Daniel Webster. If you turn it upside down and look very carefully, you will see someone else. Who do you see?

Slowly rotate this page in a circular
motion. What happens to the clown's
drum? What's unusual about
the word "rotator"?

Stare at the dot for about 30 seconds.
Try not to blink. Then look at a blank wall
or a sheet of white paper. You will see a
famous lady. Who is she?

Do you notice anything unusual about
this eaten apple? The clue is in the phrase.
What's unusual about the phrase?

This attractive landscape print holds a secret.
Can you find the landlord?

How can you get the bee to move
closer to the flower?

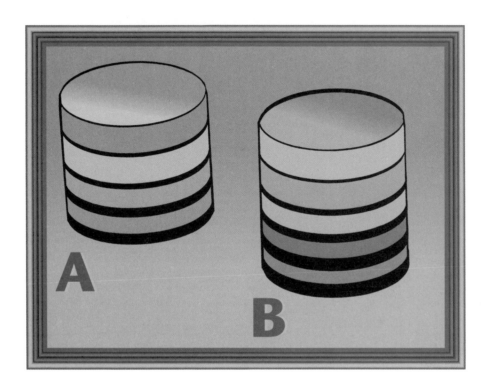

Which pile of disks has the same
height and width?

What is this a picture of?

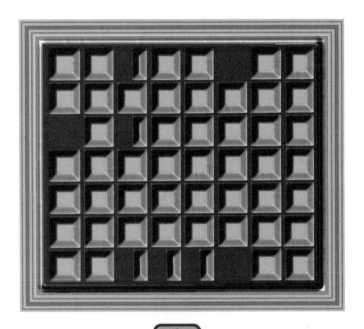

Can you discover the secret word that
has been concealed in this design?

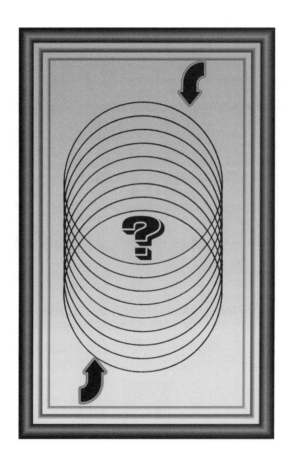

You can look through this coil
from either end. Keep staring at it
and what happens?

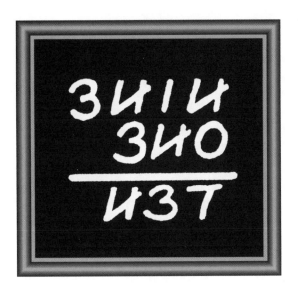

This mathematical problem is wrong.
How can you correct it?

What do you see in this
strange picture?

Can you find this baby's mother?

The soldier is pointing his finger straight at you.
Move your head from left to right.
What appears to happen?

Otto is holding a cake. One slice is missing. Can you find it? There is also something odd about the name "Otto." What is it?

Does this sign say "knowledge" or
does it say "ignorance"?

How can you get the boy to take a
spoonful of his medicine?

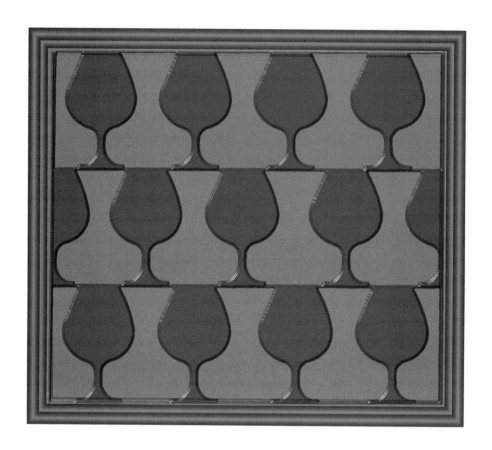

What do you see, glasses
or vases?

Will the girl ever get to the bottom
step on this flight of stairs?

Are these two painted stripes exactly the same size, or is one bigger than the other?

What bird do you see here,
a hawk or a goose?

Can you figure out what
these shapes represent?

BACCHUS

This is a picture of the Roman god
Bacchus. If you look very carefully you
will also see a picture of Romeo and
Juliet. Can you find them?

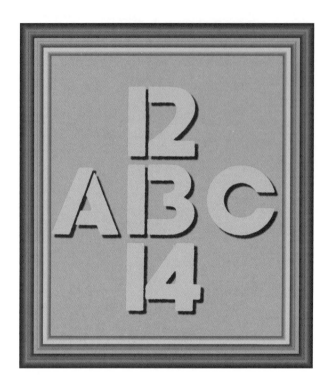

What do you see in the middle
of the frame? Is it the letter B
or the number 13?

The shapes may seem unrelated,
but they form a figure. It is
an example of a "closure." Can you
see what the figure is?

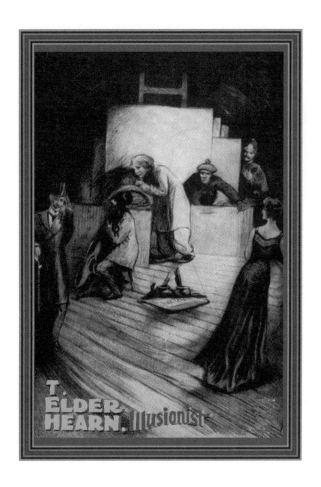

This is a poster of vaudeville
performer, T. Elder Hearn. He was a
quick-change artist. What do you see
in this publicity print?

Magician Horace Goldin used this
flyer to advertise his theater shows.
Who looks taller, Goldin as a man
or as a boy?

Stare at the dot for about
30 seconds. Try not to blink. Now
stare at a piece of white paper.
What do you see?

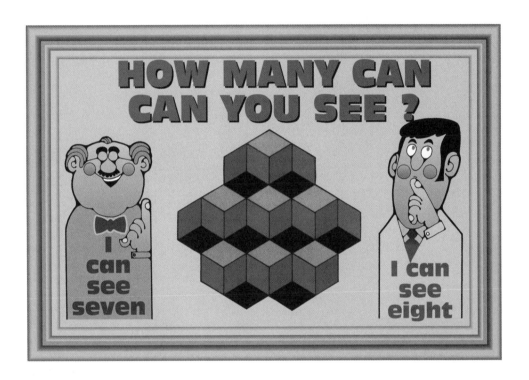

How many cubes can you see,
seven or eight?

Clowns work in the circus. Here's the
clown. Where's the circus?

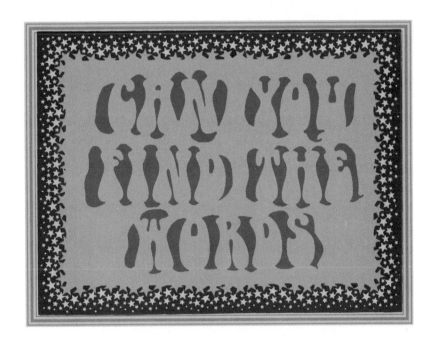

Can you find the hidden message?
What does it say?

The hooded monk has a bizarre
secret. What is it?

Can you figure out what this Victorian
puzzle shows? Is it an animal,
vegetable, or mineral? Try looking
at it from different angles.

Only one of these sets of letters says
something when viewed in a mirror.
Can you figure out which one it is
before using the mirror?

Are the three dots on the
inside or the
outside of this frame?

This picture is based on what were known in Victorian times as "Fantasy Faces." What do you see?

Is there life after death?

At first glance, we see a pig.
But where is the farmer?

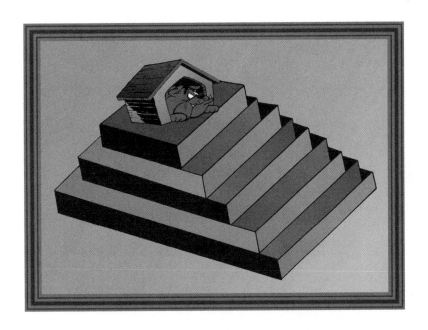

Do you notice anything
unusual about
this flight of steps?

Can you see where Napoleon
is hiding?

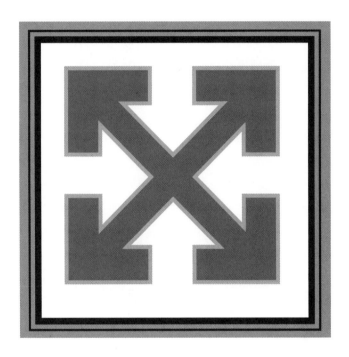

What do you see in this picture:

Gray arrows or white arrows?

Can you spot the farmer
in this landscape?

The shop was selling
poor-quality dice
at 50¢ each.
This was not the correct
price. Can you figure
out what
the real price was?

What playing card is represented in
this illustration?

The sailor is looking through his telescope to find his girlfriend. Can you find her?

This old sketch is called
"Under the Mistletoe."
What's odd about this drawing?

What's so special about
this set of numbers?

What happens when you rotate this
page in a circular motion?

What is unusual about
this sentence?

This soldier is looking for his horse.
Do you have any idea where it is?

Can you discover why this old British
colonial patriotic design is called
"The Glory of a Lion Is His Mane"?

This is the island of St. Helena.

Where is Napoleon?

Turn the page upside down and you
will see that the year 1961 still says
1961. When was the previous "upside
down" year and when will the next one occur?

What do you see in this picture?

Read the words in the hat very slowly.

What do they say?

Using only your eyes, count the
number of F's in the above sentence.
How many are there?

What do you see in this picture?

Napoleon's supporters used to wear
violets as a sign of their allegiance.
This print hides the faces of Napoleon,
Maria Louisa, and the young king of
Rome. Can you find them?

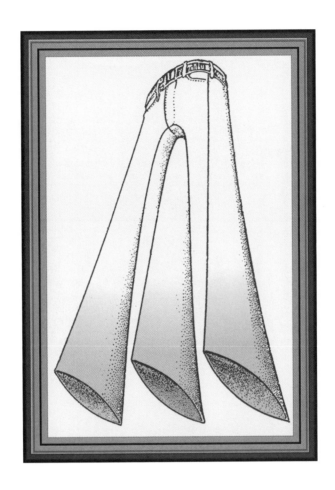

Can you see what's wrong with
this pair of bell-bottoms?

Observe this cow very carefully.
Do you notice anything unusual
about it?

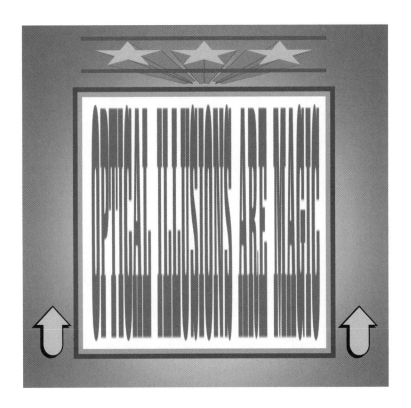

Can you read this secret message?
Tilt the page to eye level and look
in the direction of the arrows with
one eye closed.

A farmer put up this sign. Can you
understand what he was trying to say?

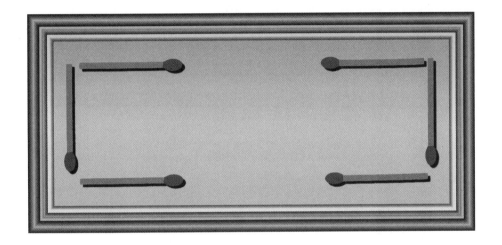

In just one move, can you
make the matches form
a complete oblong shape?

Can you see what's wrong
with this poster?

How do you turn a duck
into a rabbit?

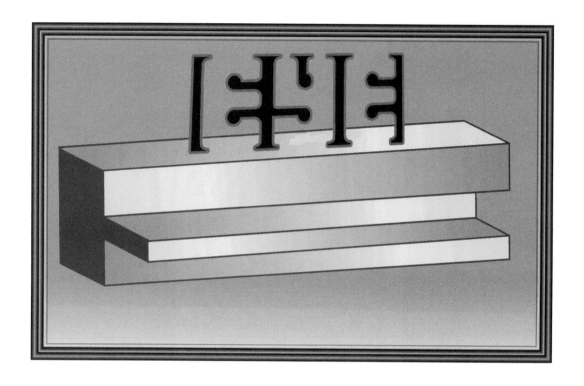

Can you figure out the meaning of the
shapes on the top shelf? And what's
unusual about the structure?

Is the star closer to the top or
the base of the mountain?

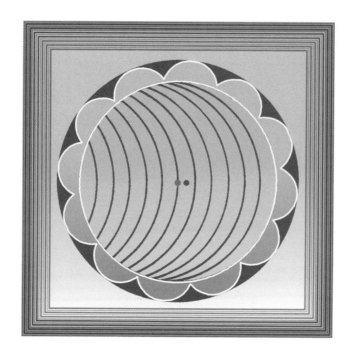

Which of these two dots
is in the true center?

The farmer's son was adding up
the large number of eggs laid over a
3-week period. Do you see anything
unusual about the answer?

Look carefully at this dog.
Can you find its master?

Without turning the page upside
down, describe this man. Is he happy
or sad? Now check to find out.

What is strange about
these donkeys?

What's wrong with this picture?

Can you spot the twenty
differences between these two
pictures?

This horse is afraid of frogs.
Can you find the frog in the stable?

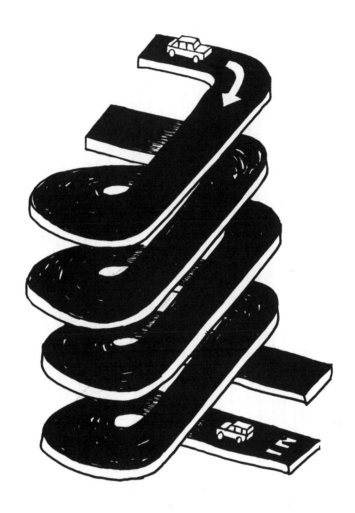

If these cars both drive at the same speed,
where will they meet?

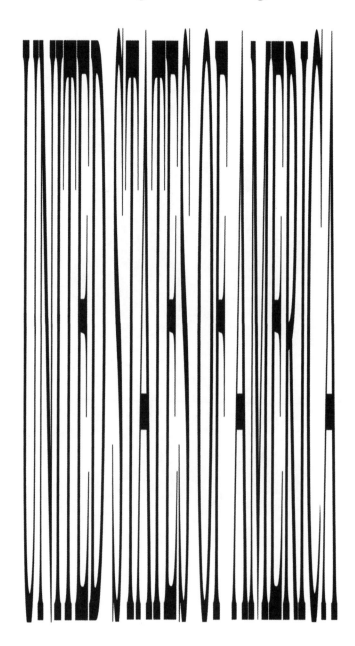

Can you read these shapes?

Are there any fakes?

This young girl will one day
be an old lady.
Can you see her in this picture?

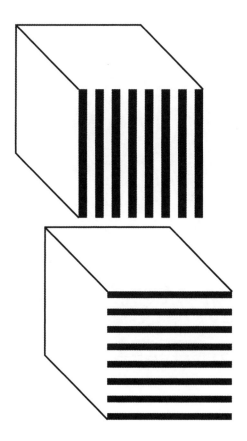

Which box is the taller of the two
and which one is the wider?

When the rescue team arrived
they found Mr. Brown and his
daughter.

Can you find their cat and dog?

The masked lady is looking for
her bearded cowboy.
Can you find him?

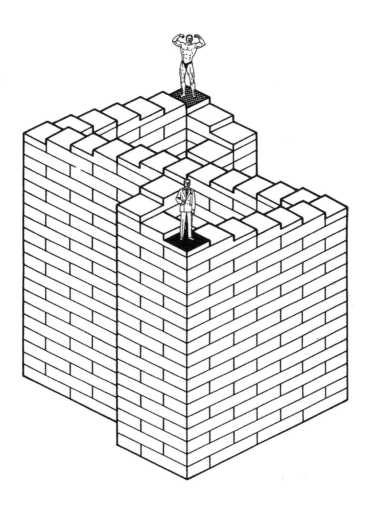

Is bodybuilder Mike higher than Scott?

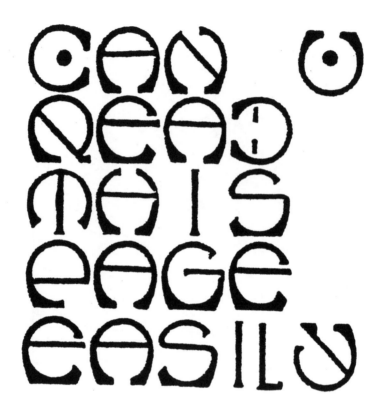

What does this message say?

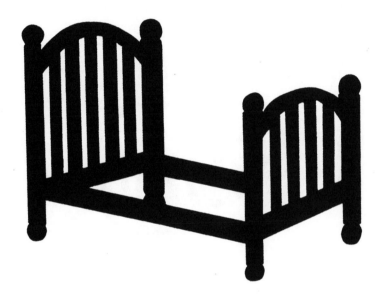

Is there something wrong with this bed?

John's watch strap had broken so he
carried the watch in his pocket.
As he entered the station his watch
showed 5:21—but he had missed
his 7:50 train. Why?

How many children can you
count in this fight?

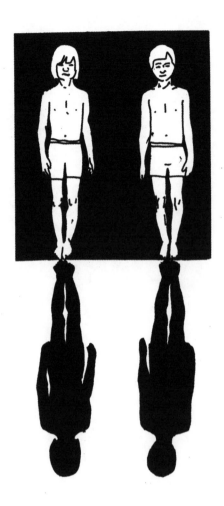

Which are bigger—the children
or their shadows?

Are these rings circular?

What do you see when you stare
at this?

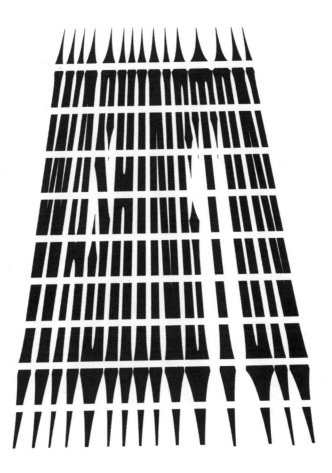

George can't read this. Can you?

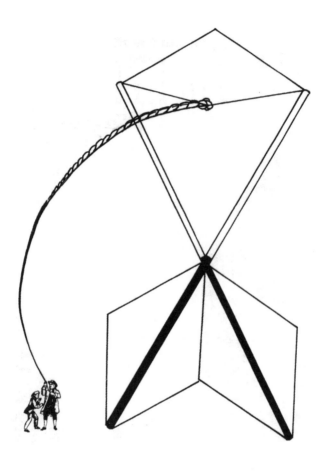

Are the black parts of the sticks
as long as the white parts?

Can you see six people admiring these flowers?

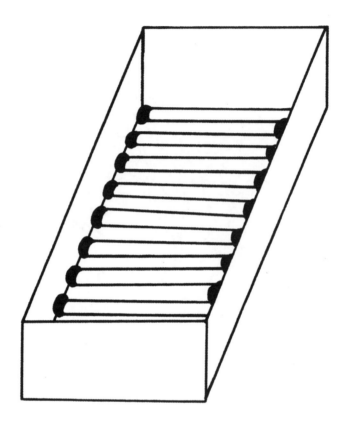

How many matches are there
in this box?

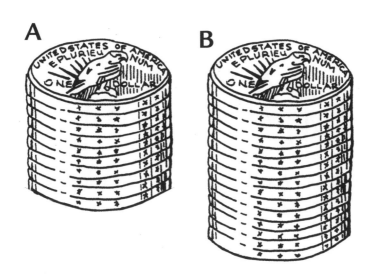

Which stack of coins is as
wide as it is tall—A or B?

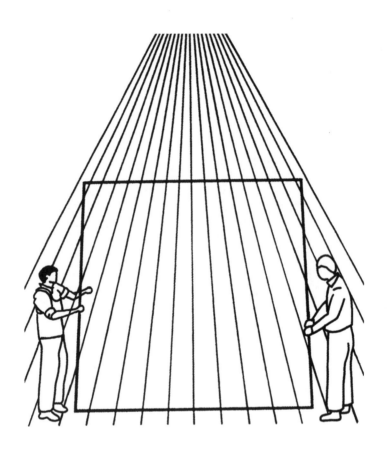

Are these men carrying a
square piece of glass?

Where is the magician?

A square box—will the hat fit in
upright or sideways?

Can you identify this country?

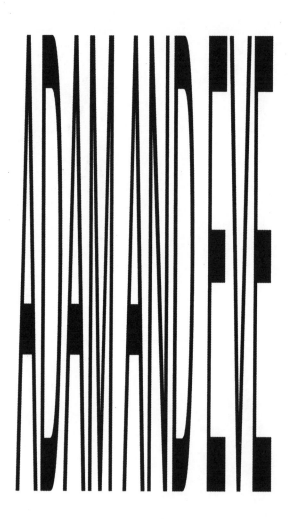

Who are these two people?

Are any of these
shapes circles?

Is the ant inside the maze
unable to get out? Is it able
to escape without climbing over a wall?

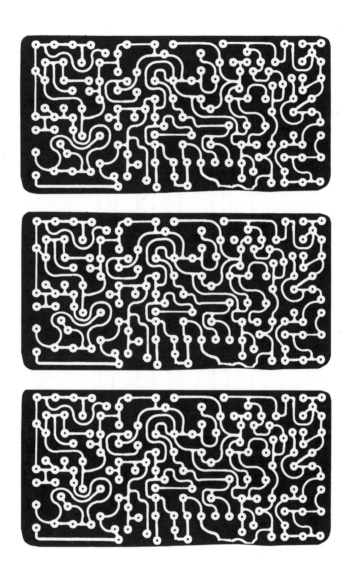

One of these printed circuits
has a fault. Can you find it?

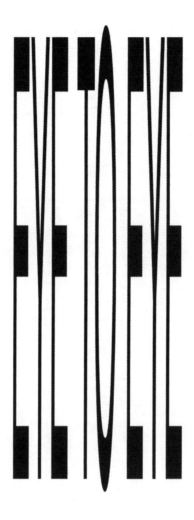

What do you see if you
agree with someone?

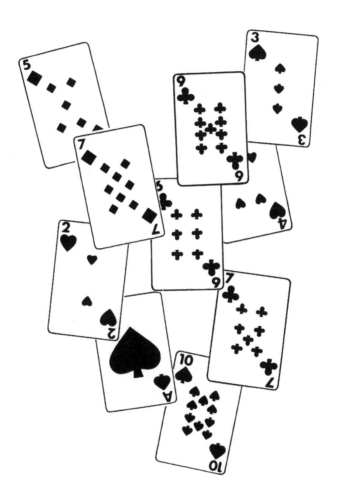

Two of these cards are forgeries, which ones?

Can you recognize this artist?

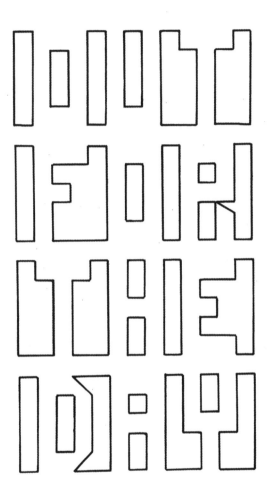

What does this sign say?

Out of these four rectangles,
which has a dot in the center?

Can you follow the spiral down to the center?

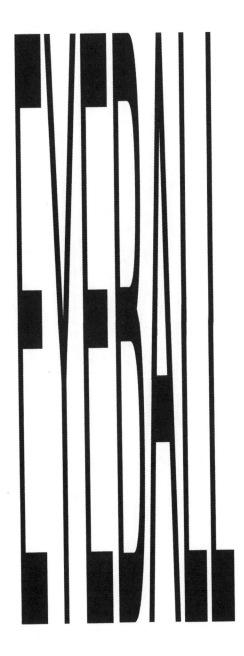

What do these shapes mean?

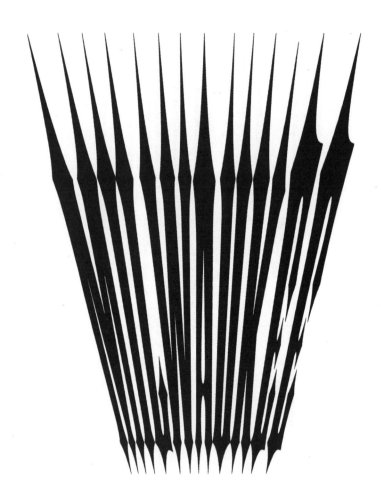

What does this shape mean?

Is this lady alone?

Which box contains two straight
vertical lines—the left or right?

Can you spot the naturalist?

Are these circles?

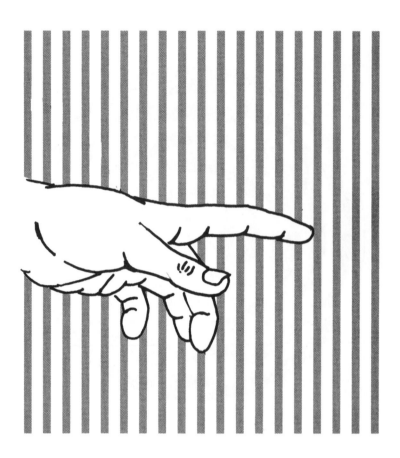

Try moving these hands closer to your eyes
and see what happens.

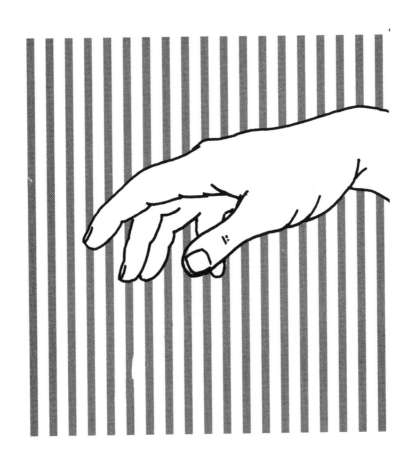

For his final examination,
Abraham produced perfectly accurate drawings
of the front and side views of a solid object.
What shape was the object?

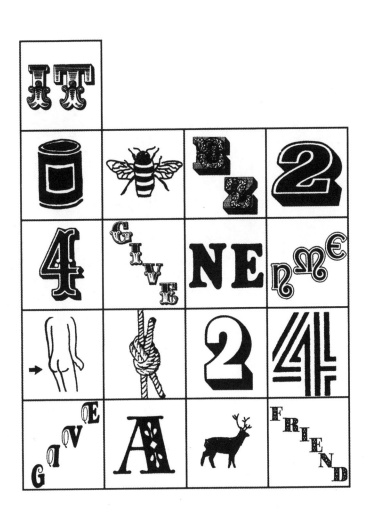

Can you read this
message?

Can you identify this country?

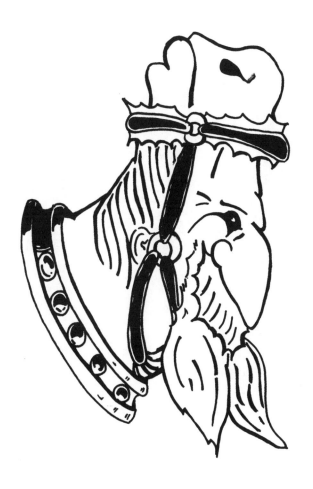

Where is the general's horse?

Do the holes on these pages spin
clockwise or counterclockwise?

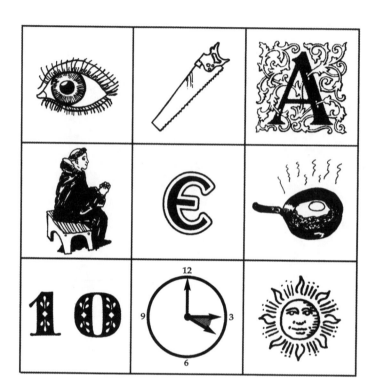

Can you read these two messages?

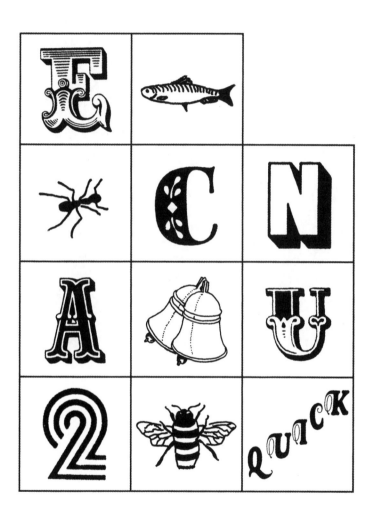

What can you see
in this pattern?

Lee says that
Ogg, the forest demon, is angry.
Kay thinks that Ogg
is happy. Who is right?

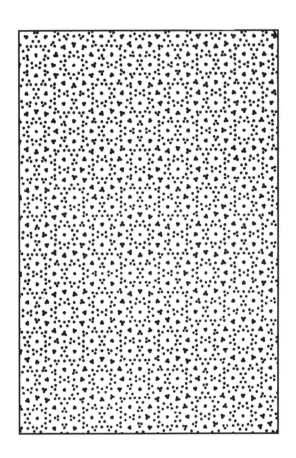

What can you see when you look at this pattern?

Could you interlock these
frames like this?

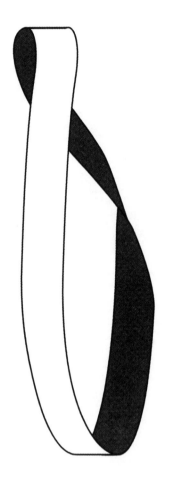

How many sides does this piece of paper have?

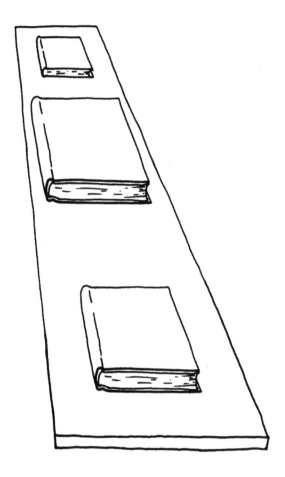

Which book is bigger than the other two?

Can you read it?

Around the disk there are thirteen baseball players. Tilt the disk and there are only twelve. Where did the other batsman go?

The shop assistant said that all of the lamps were different. Can you find two that are the same shape and pattern?

Does your brain say this figure has
gray lines across it side-to-side
and top-to-bottom?

How many letters can you
find in this pattern?

Which bomber is bigger?

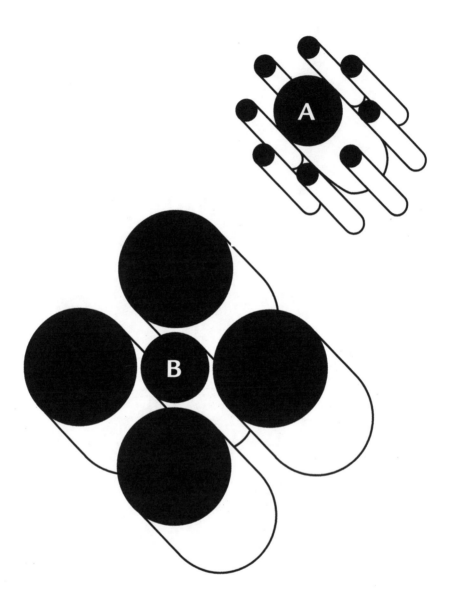

Peter had to select either A or B as the larger bucket.
Which bucket would you choose?

Are there really gray patches at the corners
of the black squares?

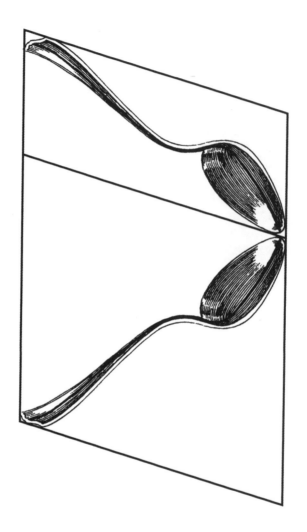

Which spoon is larger?

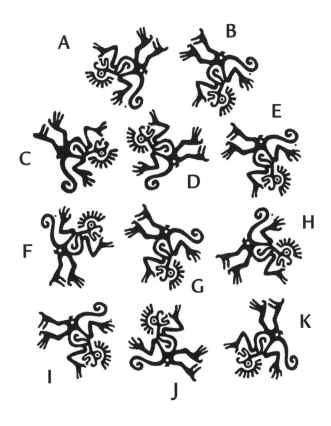

A professor in Mexico discovered a hoard of
gold rings, each one bearing the image of a
monkey. One, he decided immediately, was a
forgery. Can you spot the fake?

There are sixteen differences between this picture and the one on the next page. How many can you see?

Look at the last page. Can you find the sixteen differences?

Peter spent a long time building his shapes out of sand. On the next page are the shapes that Martha made. How are they different?

Martha did hers much quicker than Peter's did on the previous page by pressing them into the sand. What is the difference between Martha's shapes and Peter's?

There are twelve differences
between these two pictures.

Can you find them all?

Bob insists that his poles are the same
distance apart at the top and bottom.
Lauren insists her poles are too.
Who is right?

What is this?

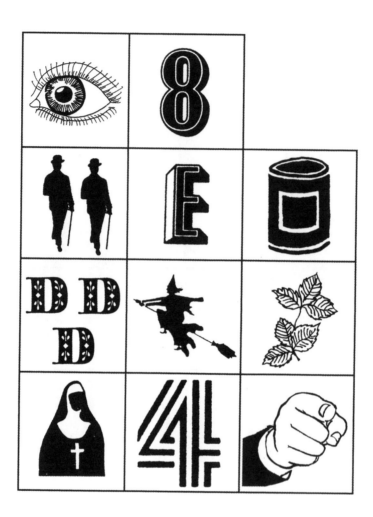

Can you read

this message?

What are the cats
trying to tell you?

We hope that you have enjoyed the optical illusions in this book. Now, a final thought. To find out what happens to all good things, just turn this page upside down.

▶ Answers ◀

Page

5   It says, "We see but we **we** don't observe."

6   The zebra is descended from a solid black animal. The white stripes are superficial tufts on the black background color of the animal's skin.

7   The old lady's face shows her life. You can see her as a baby, a young girl, courting, in marriage, and finally in death. This type of art is based on the work of Archimboldo, a painter who lived in Italy from 1517 to 1593.

8   Turn the page upside down to see them smiling. Now they are married.

9   It looks like an old Asian man. Daniel Webster's shirt forms his forehead.

10 The drum appears to spin. The word "rotator" is a palindrome; it reads the same backwards and forwards.

11 Mona Lisa.

12 Look closely and you'll find the profiles of Adam and Eve. The phrase "Madam I'm Adam" is a palindrome; it reads the same backwards and forwards.

13 Turn the page 90° counterclockwise. His face will appear.

14 Bring the page close to your face. The bee and flower will come together.

15 Pile B. Were you surprised? Measure each of them to check.

16 A black cat down a coal mine eating a stick of licorice at midnight.

17 The secret word is "hello." Look at the page in the direction of the arrow at eye level.

18   It changes direction!

19   Look at the reflection of this page in the mirror.

20   At first glance, you see a bearded man. On closer inspection, you'll find a phoenix.

21   Turn the page upside down and you will see the mother's head. The baby's diaper becomes the mother's head scarf.

22   It appears to follow you, but it's just an illusion. This design was used as a recruiting poster for the British Army.

23   Turn the page upside down and you will see a slice of cake. The name "Otto" has both horizontal and vertical symmetry. And it's also a palindrome!

24   The choice is yours!

25   Bring the page closer to your face. The figures will come together.

26   Take your pick!

27   No. The set of stairs is impossible.

28   They are both the same size. Trace one of them and measure it against the other. Their curve tricks us and creates the illusion.

29   It depends on what direction you see the bird flying. Either answer is correct.

30   The letter E. Try looking at the page from a distance.

31   The right eye and bridge of the nose form the heads of Romeo and Juliet. This form of art was popular in the 19th century in Europe.

32   The choice is yours. It all depends on what you saw first. Horizontally, it reads A, B, C. Vertically, it reads 12, 13, 14.

▶ Answers ◀

33 A person riding a horse. See picture answer 33 on page 175.

34 A part of Hearn's act is shown close-up. From a distance, it resembles the performer.

35 They are both the same height. The lines of perspective help to create the illusion of one being taller than the other.

36 The light is on! You will see a light bulb with a glowing center.

37 The choice is yours. Did you notice that the caption says, "How many can **can** you see?"

38 Turn the page 90° clockwise to reveal the circus.

39 The message, made up from the pale background shapes, says, "Can you find the words."

40 Turn the page upside down and he looks exactly the same.

41 It's a dog curled up on a rug. Turn the page so that the arrow points upwards to reveal the dog.

42 The fourth one down reads "something."

43 Your guess is as good as mine. It's impossible to tell.

44 From a distance, it's a skull. Close up, it's a man and woman sitting at a table.

45 Turn the page upside down for the answer. It says "Life."

46 Look at the left side of the picture and you will see the profile of the farmer's face.

47 Yes, it's impossible. Count the number of steps. You can count three, nine, or five steps.

48 See picture answer 48 on page 175.

49 It all depends on how you look at it.

50   Turn the page 90° counterclockwise.

51   Turn the page upside down. Then look at the reflection in a mirror and you will see the correct price is only 20¢.

52   The Three of Hearts (tree of hearts).

53   Turn the page upside down.

54   The face can belong to either the man or the woman.

55   It is a magic square. Each horizontal, vertical, and diagonal line of four numbers adds up to 264. It also works if you turn it upside down.

56   Each circle will seem to revolve on its axis. The inner cog wheel will appear to rotate in the opposite direction.

57   It is supposed to be the longest sentence that still reads the same when you turn it upside down.

58   Turn the page upside down.

59   Look at the lion's mane. You will see some of the old British colonies: Canada, India, Australia, New Zealand, and African colonies.

60   Napoleon's silhouette is found between the two trees on the right.

61   The previous one was 1881. The next one will occur in the year 6009.

62   It's a crate. See picture answer 62 on page 176. It's easier to see it with the added lines.

63   It says, "I've got a **a** big head."

64   There are six F's in the sentence.

65 You might see a medal or two people having an argument.

66 "X" marks their spot. See picture answer 66 on page 176.

67 The middle leg is impossible.

68 Look at the markings on the cow's back. You will see a map of the United Kingdom.

69 It says, "Optical illusions are magic."

70 To tie mules to.

71 Slowly bring the page closer to your face. At a certain point, the matches will join up.

72 Look at the sequence of the words. It says, "the with." It should be "with the."

73 Turn the page 90° counterclockwise.

74 The shapes spell the word "eye." The shelf is an impossible object.

75 The star is midway between the point and the base. Use a ruler and you'll see.

76 The dot that is on the line is in the center.

77 Turn the page upside down and it says, "Lots o' eggs."

78 Study the picture carefully and you'll see his face. His hat is formed from the dog's ear.

79 At first glance, we think he's happy. But he's really sad. We are not used to seeing faces upside down. Since the mouth and eyes have been inverted, he seems very weird when we look at him.

80 The three donkeys have only three ears among them!

81 Turn on the light. It's an impossible candelabra. A number of the holders seem to be suspended in midair.

82 Did you find twenty differences? Check picture answer 82 on page 177.

84 Turn the page so that the right-hand side is at the bottom and you will see the frog.

85 The cars will not meet because they are on different ramps.

86 It reads: "UNITED STATES OF AMERICA" Turn the page so that the bottom edge is at eye level and look across the page.

87 The top bill reads "10 DOLLARS" and the others read "TEN DOLLARS." Check picture answer 87 on page 178.

88 Maybe you see the old lady and have difficulty seeing the young girl.

89 Both are the same size.

90 The cat and dog are hard to find. If you can't do it, check them out in picture answers 90 and 91 on page 179.

92 Turn her upside down.

93 If Scott turns to his left, he walks down to Mike. If he turns to his right, he walks up to Mike.

94 The strange shapes read: "CAN U READ THIS PAGE EASILY?"

95 The end near the head has five upright bars. The end near the foot only has four, but the gaps and the bars are the same width at both ends.

96 He was reading an upside-down watch. Turn the page around to read the real time.

97 If you count the heads there are five children, but if you count

the bodies there are ten. Check it out in picture answer 97 on page 180.

98 The children are the same size as their shadows.

99 They are circles but the background makes them appear to be flattened.

100 The pattern sends out spiraling waves.

101 Hold the top edge close to your eyes and look across the page. It is George's name—WASHINGTON.

102 The black parts are the same length as the white parts of the sticks.

103 Turn the page around to see them all. Check your discoveries with picture answer 103 on page 181.

104 Eight if you count the match heads on the left and only seven if you count those on the right.

105 The stack marked B.

106 No, it is much narrower at the top.

107 Turn the page upside down.

108 The hat fits in either way because it is just as high as it is wide.

109 If you look from the top edge of the page you can see a map of the U.S.

110 If you look from the bottom of the page at an acute angle you should be able to read the words "ADAM AND EVE."

111 None of the shapes are circles.

112 The ant is able to get out of the maze without climbing a wall. To find out how, look at picture answer 112 on page 182.

113 The middle circuit has the fault. See picture answer 113 on page 183.

114 If you look from the bottom of the page at an acute angle you should be able to read the words "EYE TO EYE."

115 The seven of diamonds has eight diamonds in the center and the nine of clubs has its bottom number upside down, so they are both fake.

116 The picture is of Vincent Van Gogh.

117 It reads: "OUT FOR THE DAY." See picture answer 117 on page 184.

118 The third rectangle from the left is the only one with the dot in the center.

120 There is no spiral. They are concentric circles that guide your eye to the center.

121 If you look from the bottom edge of the page you should see the word "EYEBALL."

122 Position the page so that the top is farther away and you should see the word "MILWAUKEE."

123 There are two men's heads on either side of her head. Look at picture answer 123 on page 185.

124 The box on the left has straight, vertical lines.

126 If you turn the page upside down you should see a head on the butterfly's wing. If you can't, look at picture answer 126 on page 186.

127 No, they are not circles.

128 The outstretched fingers touch.

130   The solution is clear in picture answer 130 on page 187.

131   The message reads: "It can be easy to forgive any enemy, but not to forgive a dear friend."

132   Turn the book upside down and look from the bottom right corner of the page to see Britain.

133   Turn the page upside down to see a horse.

134   You can see them spiraling either way—it depends whether you see them going away from you or coming toward you.

136   The first message reads: "I SAW A MONKEY FRIGHTEN OUR SON"; and the second message reads: "EFFICIENCY ENABLES YOU TO BE QUICK."

138   You should see a spherical bulge forming in the center.

139   Turn the page upside down to see a different person.

140   You should see many different-sized circles overlapping and intertwining.

141   It's impossible to construct such a shape.

142   It has only one side.

143   None. The bottom two books are the same size.

144   Look across the page from the bottom edge. It reads: "EYE OPENER."

145   This is a famous trick invented by Sam Loyd. The legs, arms, and bodies on the disk match up with those on the outside; however, when the disk is turned, the parts still match but make one figure less.

146   The second lamp on the left in the top row and the second from last in the second row.

147   As the black and white shapes get smaller and smaller, they seem to get less distinct and form gray areas.

148   Six letters: W M H E G O. I bet you forgot about the encircling O.

149   The bomber on the top is bigger.

150   Both the buckets are the same size.

151   The regular pattern of black squares with narrow white spaces between them form, in your mind's eye, gray patches at the corners of the black squares.

152   Both spoons are the same size.

153   The monkey labeled C. All the monkeys hold their left hands up to their mouths, monkey C holds his right hand up.

154   Can you find the sixteen changes before you look at picture answer 154 on page 188?

156   Both patterns are exactly the same. Peter's look as though they are built up and Martha's pressed into the sand because the shadows are positioned differently.

158   How many did you find? Check your discoveries against picture answer 158 on page 189.

160   Bob. Lauren's poles are farther apart at the top.

161   Hold the lower edge close to your eyes, look across the page, and you will see six cats.

162   The message reads: "I ate too many candies which leaves none for you"

163   The cats' tails spell: "THE END."

164   It says: "The end."

33

48

62

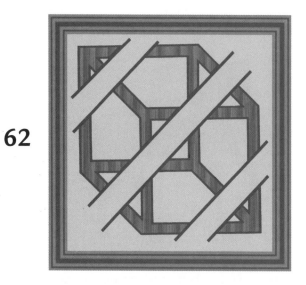

66

82

87

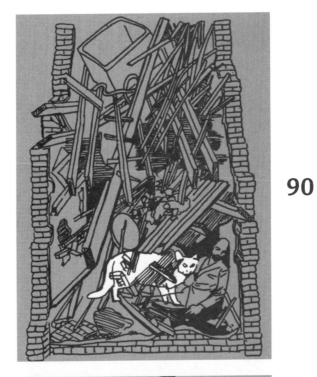

90

91

97

103

Cover half the maze with a sheet of paper, then count the number of lines from the middle to the outside of the maze. If you get an even number, the ant can crawl out, if odd, he must cross a line. This solution works for all closed mazes of this type.

112

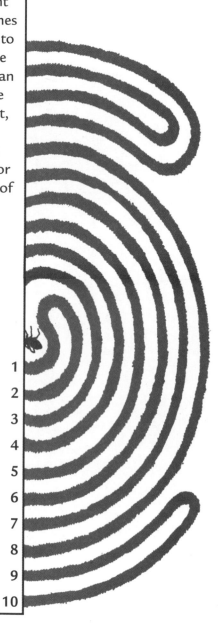

1
2
3
4
5
6
7
8
9
10

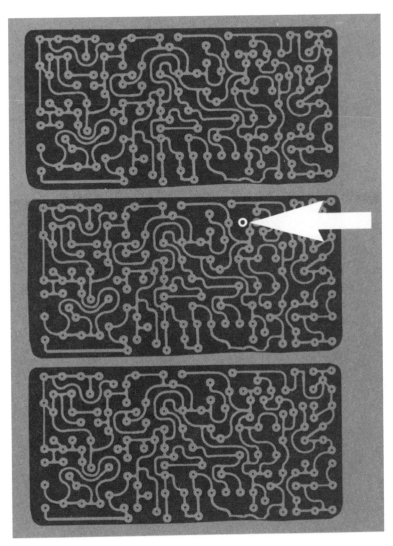

113

117

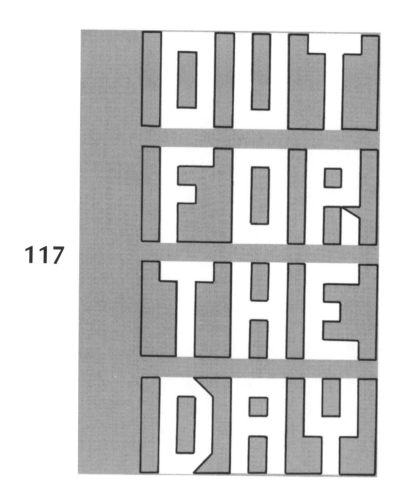

123

126

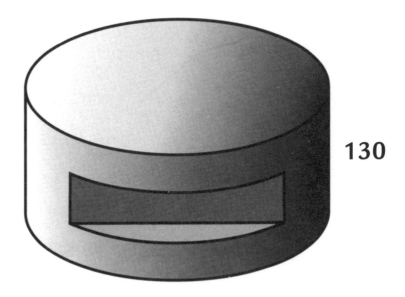

130

154

158

Note: *Italicized* page numbers
indicate answers.